"Be Courageous"

2018 Convention of Jehovah's Witnesses

Name:_____

Dates:_____

Congregation:_____

Personal goals 2018:

Spiritual goals 2018:

My favorite speaker:

My favorite video:

My favorite talk:

New points to use in ministry:

Location:

Comment/Note:

Attendance:

Friday

Saturday

Sunday

Friday

"Be courageous and very strong"
~ Joshua 1:7

9:40 CHAIRMAN'S ADDRESS: Jehovah - The Source of True Courage

Speaker:

Favorite Point:

Theme Scripture(s):

WHY AND **HOW** IS JEHOVAH THE TRUE SOURCE OF COURAGE?

Main Points / Scriptures	NOTES
•	
•	
•	
•	
•	
•	
•	
•	

Something New I Learned:_____

Friday - *"Be courageous and very strong"* - Joshua 1:7

10:10 SYMPOSIUM: Why True Christians Need Courage - TO PREACH

Speaker:

Favorite Point:

Theme Scripture(s):

WHY DOES PREACHING REQUIRE COURAGE? HOW CAN I BOOST MY COURAGE?

Main Points / Scriptures	NOTES

Self Evaluation **(Am I courageous?):**

5

10:10 SYMPOSIUM: Why True Christians Need Courage - TO REMAIN HOLY

Speaker:

Theme Scripture(s):

Favorite Point:

WHAT DOES IT MEAN TO REMAIN HOLY?

Main Points / Scriptures

-
-
-

NOTES

SYMPOSIUM: Why True Christians Need Courage - TO REMAIN HOLY

B E C O U R A G E O U S

 What is the key to remaining holy?

10:10 SYMPOSIUM: Why True Christians Need Courage - TO MAINTAIN NEUTRALITY

Speaker:

Favorite Point:

Theme Scripture(s):

HOW COULD MY NEUTRALITY POSSIBLY BE TESTED?

Scriptures	Main Points

NOTES

Am I prepared to defend my neutrality?_____

11:15 DRAMATIC BIBLE READING: "BE COURAGEOUS AND STRONG AND GO TO WORK!"

Speaker:

Favorite Point:

Theme Scripture(s):

HOW CAN I "GO TO WORK"?

SUMMARY POINTS

1.

2.

3.

4.

5.

• SKETCH SPACE •

THIS BIBLE READING HAS MOTIVATED ME TO:

8 Something NEW I learned:_____

11:45 "No Weapon Formed Against You Will Have Any Success"

Speaker:

Favorite Point:

Theme Scripture(s):

HOW DOES THIS SUBJECT **BUILD YOUR CONFIDENCE IN JEHOVAH?**

Main Points / Scriptures	NOTES

What are these "weapons"?_____

JWWorksheets.com

IG:@JWDownloads

JW-Downloads.com

"No Weapon Formed Against You Will Have Any Success"

1:40 SYMPOSIUM: Courage Weakeners vs Courage Strengtheners
DESPAIR VS HOPE

Speaker:

Favorite Point:

Theme Scripture(s):

HOW DOES HOPE PREVAIL OVER DESPAIR?

Main Points - Talk Summary

NOTES

SCRIPTURES

Something New I Learned:_____

Friday - *"**Be courageous and very strong**"* - Joshua 1:7

1:40 SYMPOSIUM - COMPLAINT VS THANKSGIVING

Speaker:

Favorite Point:

Theme Scripture(s):

Benefits of Complaining

Benefits of Thanksgiving

Scriptures

Main Points

Notes

Do I COMPLAIN or GIVE THANKS more often?_____

1:40 SYMPOSIUM: UNWHOLESOME RECREATION VS FIELD MINISTRY

Speaker:

Favorite Point:

Theme Scripture(s):

HOW DO YOU FEEL ABOUT PARTICIPATION IN THE FIELD MINISTRY?

Main Points / Scriptures	NOTES
•	
•	
•	
•	
•	
•	
•	
•	

SYMPOSIUM: Courage Weakeners vs Courage Strengtheners - UNWHOLESOME RECREATION vs FIELD MINISTRY

Friday - *"Be courageous and very strong"* - Joshua 1:7

1:40 SYMPOSIUM: BAD ASSOCIATIONS vs GOOD ASSOCIATIONS

Speaker: _____

Favorite Point:

Theme Scripture(s): _____

WHAT EFFECTS DO GOOD ASSOCIATIONS HAVE ON YOU?

Main Points / Scriptures	NOTES

Why must bad assocations be avoided?: _____

1:40 SYMPOSIUM: WORLDLY WISDOM vs PERSONAL STUDY

Speaker:

Favorite Point:

Theme Scripture(s):

HOW HAS PERSONAL STUDY CHANGED YOUR LIFE?

Scriptures

- _____
- _____
- _____
- _____
- _____
- _____
- _____

NOTES

Talk Summary

14 Why is worldly wisdom lacking? _____

1:40 SYMPOSIUM: Courage Weakeners vs Courage Strengtheners
DOUBT vs FAITH

Speaker:

Favorite Point:

Theme Scripture(s):

HOW DOES FAITH STRENGTHEN YOUR COURAGE?

Main Points - Talk Summary

NOTES

SCRIPTURES

Something New I Learned:

3:20 SYMPOSIUM: What They Risked; How They Were Rewarded

Speaker:

Favorite Point:

Theme Scripture(s):

HOW CAN I SHOW SIMILAR FAITH TO THESE BIBLE CHARACTERS?

HANANIAH, MISHAEL, and AZARIAH

Main Points / Scriptures	Hananiah, Mishael and Azariah
•	
•	
•	
•	
•	
•	
•	
•	

16 What did they risk?:

COURAGEOUS

Friday - *"Be courageous and very strong"* - Joshua 1:7

3:20 SYMPOSIUM: What They Risked; How They Were Rewarded

Speaker:

Favorite Point:

Theme Scripture(s):

WHAT WAS SPECIAL ABOUT AQUILA AND PRISCILLA?

Main Points / Scriptures	Aquila and Priscilla

AQUILA NAD PRISCILLA

Self Evaluation **(Am I courageous like Aquila and Priscilla?):**

3:20 SYMPOSIUM: What They Risked; How They Were Rewarded

Speaker:

Favorite Point:

Theme Scripture(s):

HOW DOES STEPHEN'S EXAMPLE GIVE YOU COURAGE NOW?

STEPHEN

Main Points

-
-
-

Stephen

Scriptures

3:55 "Take Courage! I Have Conquered the World"

Speaker:

Favorite Point:

Theme Scripture(s):

HOW HAS THE WORLD "ALREADY BEEN CONQUERED"?

Scriptures

Main Points

Notes

_____

_____

_____

_____

_____

_____

_____

_____

_____

Describe your level of courage after this part _____

4:15 Courageous Soldiers of Christ

Speaker:

Favorite Point:

Theme Scripture(s):

WHO ARE THE "COURAGEOUS SOLDIERS OF CHRIST"?

Courageous Soldiers of Christ

Main Points / Scriptures	NOTES

How important is being courageous now?_____

```
D L E I F Y Q S T R O N G D D H V J Q H T V G O O
A H T Z X T S M C H C T E E Y X K W G Z E A X W E
F H I E P I U T A A R L D H A V O H E J R M M U F
J Y Y C B L U X R V N R E S R N O I T N E V N O C
R S F R J A F S W E A Y R T S I N I M H L Q M J D
L S B U Y R V R G W N Q N O P A E W E F K U B E J
G E J O I T P L E B F G U E P P D X V K I W E G X
I C L S S U R R L F J A T P G M I H O S X E F A K
W C J N H E I C D S G N W H F E H O O E G A M R H
C U H B P N S H E G R O P X E O C P M V Z K O U L
H S J J S E C C L K G N O T V N M J S T L E C O N
A E J C C I A B Y G N Z D M Y E L R C G N T C S
I C F W M J L E I G F E I K S H B D E T P E P W N
R J A Z I H L R B Y X S P V C Q X C I C Y D O G O
M E T T H Y A P E Y R F C D I T I T D Q E P O H I
A T R C H R I S T I A N S I R G H D L E C T Z A T
N U W X O K H H W C H R I S T A S X O P I O G I A
E K O K Q U F A O A K M E L R C M K S U S L M R I
Y N N E R E R N N L D E Y E C D U A N Z U W A A C
A S C E Y O Q A J A Y G A N E U W V T A M H D Z O
X O E S H U W A G R N D V S S L L Y X I H S D A S
O S O Q E P F D I E I I P A L I U Q A T C T R A S
J I I R P C E B A N O A A M I S H A E L N N E Q A
P Q E M Y C G T G J I U M H Y Z W I Q U O D S X L
O D G Q X W X P S R P U S V A Q O U L U G R S N Q
```

Address	Christians	Field	Mishael	Soldiers	Thanksgiving
Aquila	Conquered	Good	Music	Source	True
Associations	Convention	Hananiah	Neurtrality	Stephen	Weakened
Azariah	Courage	Holy	Preach	Strengthened	Weapon
Bible	Courageous	Hope	Priscilla	Strong	Work
Chairman	Despair	Jehovah	Reading	Success	
Christ	Dramatic	Ministry	Rewarded	Symposium	

What was the theme scripture for Friday?

Who were the six characters discussed in the symposium about risks and rewards?

How does FAITH win over DOUBT?

Why do we need courage to maintain neutrality?

FRIDAY REVIEW

B
E
C
O
U
R
A
G
E
O
U
S

Saturday

"Showing all the more courage to speak the word of God fearlessly"

- Philippians 1:14

9:40 SYMPOSIUM: Be a Courageous... BIBLE STUDENT

Speaker:

Favorite Point:

Theme Scripture(s):

WHAT CAN I DO TO BE A COURAGEOUS BIBLE STUDENT?

Scriptures

- _____
- _____
- _____
- _____
- _____
- _____
- _____

NOTES

Talk Summary

9:40 SYMPOSIUM: Be a Courageous... YOUTH

Speaker:

Favorite Point:

Theme Scripture(s):

TIPS ON HOW TO BE COURAGEOUS WHETHER OR NOT YOU ARE A YOUTH:

Main Points / Scriptures	NOTES

A single point I want to remember:

Ps 71:5 - How have you trusted in Jehovah since your youth? :_____

9:40 SYMPOSIUM: Be a Courageous... PUBLISHER

Speaker:

Favorite Point:

Theme Scripture(s):

SMALL STEPS I CAN TAKE TO BE MORE COURAGEOUS AS A PUBLISHER:

Main Points

-
-
-

Scriptures

_____

_____

_____

_____

NOTES

1 thing that requires courage in the ministry:_____

9:40 SYMPOSIUM: Be a Courageous... MARRIAGE MATE

Speaker:

Favorite Point:

Theme Scripture(s):

How I am courageous now:

How I can improve:

Scriptures

Main Points

Notes

Is Jehovah happy about the way I treat my family/friends?_____

JWWorksheets.com

IG:@JWDownloads

JW-Downloads.com

SYMPOSIUM: Be a Courageous... MARRIAGE MATE

9:40 SYMPOSIUM: Be a Courageous... PARENT

Speaker:

Favorite Point:

Theme Scripture(s):

HOW CAN I BE A **BETTER** PARENT? (OR HELP YOUNG ONES IN THE CONGREGATION?)

Main Points & Scriptures

NOTES

9:40 SYMPOSIUM: Be a Courageous... PIONEER

Speaker:

Favorite Point:

Theme Scripture(s):

MINISTRY GOALS THIS YEAR:

WHY DO YOU NEED COURAGE IN THE MINISTRY?

Scriptures

NOTES

Main Points + Talk Summary

Self Evaluation HOW CAN I INCREASE MY MINISTRY?:_____

9:40 SYMPOSIUM: Be a Courageous... CONGREGATION ELDER

Speaker:

Favorite Point:

Theme Scripture(s):

HOW CAN I SHOW **MORE** APPRECIATION FOR THE ELDERS IN MY CONGREGATION?

Scriptures	Scriptures	Scriptures	Talk Summary

NOTES

Saturday - *"Showing all the more courage to speak the word of God fearlessly"* - Philippians 1:14

9:40 Symposium: Be a Courageous... OLDER PERSON

Speaker:

Favorite Point:

Theme Scripture(s):

What can I PERSONALLY DO to help the older ones in my congregation?

Main Points / Scriptures	NOTES

How am I taking care of the elderly in my family?_____

NOT THE TEN CHIEFTAINS, BUT JOSHUA AND CALEB

BE COURAGEOUS

11:00 Symposium: Imitate, Not the Cowards, But the Courageous

Speaker:

Favorite Point:

Theme Scripture(s):

WHY ARE JOSHUA AND CALEB SUCH EXCELLENT EXAMPLES?

Scriptures	Main Points

Notes

32 Why are the 10 chieftans a bad example?_____

11:00 SYMPOSIUM: Imitate, Not the Cowards, But the Courageous

Speaker:

Favorite Point:

Theme Scripture(s):

WHO WAS JAEL?

Main Points / Scriptures	NOTES
•	
•	
•	

Personal Goal - What can I do like Jael?_____

NOT THE INHABITANTS OF MEROZ, BUT JAEL

11:00 Symposium: Imitate, Not the Cowards, But the Courageous

Speaker:

Favorite Point:

Theme Scripture(s):

WHAT ACTIONS PROVED MICAIAH TO BE COURAGEOUS?

NOT THE FALSE PROPHETS, BUT MICAIAH

Main Points / Scriptures

-
-
-
-
-
-
-
-

NOTES

B
E
C
O
U
R
A
G
E
O
U
S

What other qualities of Micaiah do you want to imitate?:_____

11:00 SYMPOSIUM: Imitate, Not the Cowards, But the Courageous

Speaker:

Favorite Point:

Theme Scripture(s):

HOW WAS JEREMIAH COURAGEOUS?

Main Points & Scriptures

NOTES

NOT URIJAH, BUT JEREMIAH

11:00 Symposium: Imitate, Not the Cowards, But the Courageous

Speaker:

Favorite Point:

Theme Scripture(s):

What distinguished PAUL from the rich young ruler?

Scriptures	Scriptures	Scriptures	Talk Summary

NOTES

36 How would imitating Paul improve MY life?_____

11:45 BAPTISM: "We Are Not The Sort Who Shrink Back"!

Speaker:

Favorite Point:

Theme Scripture(s):

LISTEN FOR A **NEW** OR ESPECIALLY **INTERESTING POINT** IN THIS BAPTISM TALK:

Main Points / Scriptures	NOTES
•	
•	
•	
•	
•	
•	
•	
•	

What does it mean to "shrink back"? _____

BAPTISM: "We Are Not The Sort Who Shrink Back"!

1:50 Symposium: Learn Courage From Creation - LIONS

Speaker:

Favorite Point:

Theme Scripture(s):

How are LIONS courageous?

Main Points / Scriptures	NOTES

How is MY courage compared to a lion?_____

Saturday - *"**Showing all the more courage to speak the word of God fearlessly**"* - Philippians 1:14

1:50 SYMPOSIUM: Learn Courage From Creation - HORSES

Speaker:

Favorite Point:

Theme Scripture(s):

What situations require horses to be courageous?

How can I APPLY this in MY life?

Scriptures

Main Points

Notes

My favorite thing about horses is_____

1:50 SYMPOSIUM: Learn Courage From Creation - MONGOOSES

Speaker:

Favorite Point:

Theme Scripture(s):

SOMETHING **NEW** I LEARNED ABOUT MONGOOSES:

ALTHOUGH SMALL, HOW ARE THEY COURAGEOUS?

Scriptures

NOTES

Main Points + Talk Summary

40 Describe a mongoose:_____

1:50 SYMPOSIUM: Learn Courage From Creation - HUMMINGBIRDS

Speaker:

Favorite Point:

Theme Scripture(s):

WHY DO YOU THINK HUMMINGBIRDS WERE INCLUDED IN THIS SYMPOSIUM?

Main Points & Scriptures

NOTES

JWWorksheets.com

IG:@JWDownloads

JW-Downloads.com

1:50 SYMPOSIUM: Learn Courage From Creation - ELEPHANTS

Speaker:

Favorite Point:

Theme Scripture(s):

SOMETHING NEW I LEARNED ABOUT ELEPHANTS:

Main Points / Scriptures	NOTES
•	
•	
•	
•	
•	
•	
•	
•	

How are elephants courageous?:

2:50 SYMPOSIUM: How Our Brothers Are Showing Courage in... AFRICA

Speaker:

Favorite Point:

Theme Scripture(s):

WHAT SPECIAL CHALLENGES DO MY BROTHERS IN AFRICA FACE?

Scriptures	Scriptures	Scriptures	Talk Summary

NOTES

How do my living conditions compare?

2:50 Symposium: How Our Brothers Are Showing Courage in... ASIA

Speaker:

Theme Scripture(s):

Favorite Point:

MAJOR TRIALS/ISSUES IN ASIA:

Scriptures	Main Points

Notes

Summary of an experience:

SYMPOSIUM: How Our Brothers Are Showing Courage in . . . ASIA

B E C O U R A G E O U S

2:50 SYMPOSIUM: How Our Brothers Are Showing Courage in... EUROPE

Speaker:

Favorite Point:

Theme Scripture(s):

WHY IS COURAGE REQUIRED FOR OUR BROTHERS IN EUROPE?

Main Points / Scriptures

-
-
-

NOTES

What countries are mentioned?

2:50 SYMPOSIUM: How Our Brothers Are Showing Courage in... NORTH AMERICA

Speaker:

Favorite Point:

Theme Scripture(s):

HOW HAS THIS TALK BUILT UP **YOUR** COURAGE?

Main Points / Scriptures

-
-
-
-
-
-
-
-

NOTES

One challenge faced by North Americans:_____

2:50 SYMPOSIUM: How Our Brothers Are Showing Courage in... OCEANIA

Speaker:

Favorite Point:

Theme Scripture(s):

WHAT CIRCUMSTANCES DO OUR BROTHERS IN OCEANIA FACE?

Main Points & Scriptures

NOTES

Something New I Learned:

2:50 SYMPOSIUM: How Our Brothers Are Showing Courage in... SOUTH AMERICA

Speaker:

Favorite Point:

Theme Scripture(s):

WHY IS COURAGE NEEDED FOR JEHOVAH'S PEOPLE IN SOUTH AMERICA?

Main Points

-
-
-

NOTES

Scriptures

_____

_____

_____

_____

Name 5 countries in South America:_____

4:15 Courageous but Not Self-Reliant!

Speaker:

Favorite Point:

Theme Scripture(s):

What is self-reliance?	What/Who do I need to rely on?

Scriptures

Main Points

Notes

Someone in my congregation I can encourage/build up:_____

JWWorksheets.com

IG:@JWDownloads

JW-Downloads.com

Courageous but Not Self-Reliant!

Africa	Europe	Older
America	Fearless	Parent
Asia	Horses	Paul
Baptism	Hummingbirds	Pioneer
Bible	Jael	Prayer
Caleb	Jeremiah	Publisher
Congregation	Joshua	Saturday
Courage	Lions	Song
Courage	Marriage	Student
Courageous	Micaiah	Video
Creation	Mongooses	Youth
Elder	Music	
Elephants	Oceania	

```
S  O  N  G  G  J  W  C  B  E  L  A  C  Y  O  U  T  H  P  N  L  L  O
L  S  D  F  P  R  Y  I  D  J  L  M  M  A  I  C  O  O  K  X  H  O  L
H  H  C  N  U  G  B  S  C  M  H  P  B  S  E  U  R  O  P  E  E  P  D
A  U  C  V  B  F  F  U  O  R  L  D  R  N  I  N  D  D  Q  D  A  A  E
I  T  D  B  L  F  E  M  U  T  E  R  N  S  O  T  E  A  I  J  K  R  R
A  A  M  G  I  L  F  X  R  P  Y  A  S  I  T  E  P  V  Q  E  Y  E  X
C  Y  J  W  S  U  T  H  A  U  M  C  T  F  O  W  A  A  J  B  M  N  C
I  P  O  Z  H  A  M  I  G  O  F  A  U  I  L  R  T  F  B  L  A  T  B
M  H  S  Y  E  O  N  Q  E  E  G  J  D  C  O  U  R  A  G  E  O  U  S
S  R  H  D  R  A  L  L  A  E  S  Y  E  M  N  D  Z  G  G  O  D  L
A  Z  U  S  E  D  E  R  R  C  E  T  N  U  R  A  S  A  E  P  V  D  L
T  O  A  C  P  A  L  G  N  H  S  V  T  P  E  D  R  E  F  O  J  K  O
U  A  O  Z  J  E  N  E  E  Z  R  J  K  E  E  Z  G  R  M  R  U  O  S
R  S  G  T  S  O  K  M  G  L  O  H  E  Q  N  T  G  K  I  I  I  J  N
D  Z  E  S  C  Y  J  D  R  H  H  G  P  K  O  S  J  R  K  A  A  C  Y
A  L  K  S  V  N  H  U  M  M  I  N  G  B  I  R  D  S  E  C  G  L  A
Y  I  I  S  O  D  A  A  S  I  A  X  E  N  P  R  Q  V  I  Y  I  E  R
A  O  T  Z  M  O  L  Y  R  K  B  C  L  Z  N  Z  B  R  G  X  A  Z  A
P  N  I  J  B  B  G  E  L  C  I  W  D  S  C  X  E  V  F  N  V  R  B
A  S  K  E  F  F  D  N  L  R  B  T  N  N  Y  M  Z  P  P  M  A  P  P
U  O  Y  C  I  L  O  P  O  H  L  Q  Z  H  A  I  M  E  R  E  J  D  H
L  L  V  M  E  C  I  R  N  M  E  A  B  B  R  O  C  X  A  J  P  O  V
H  D  M  I  S  T  N  A  H  P  E  L  E  O  T  C  O  U  R  A  G  E  K
```

SATURDAY REVIEW

What was the theme scripture for Saturday?

Name 6 of the 8 individuals reviewed in the 9:40 Symposium, "Be a Courageous..."

Who were the courageous ones (6) we are encouraged to imitate in the 11:00 Symposium?

What 5 animals did we learn courage from?

How are our brothers showing courage in South America?

B
E
C
O
U
R
A
G
E
O
U
S

Sunday

"Be courageous and strong of heart. Yes, hope in Jehovah." -Psalm 27: 14

9:40 The Cry of "Peace and Security!"

Speaker:

Favorite Point:

Theme Scripture(s):

1 THESS 5:3 GIVES WHAT INDICATION OF HOW QUICKLY DESTRUCTION WILL COME?

Main Points / Scriptures	NOTES
•	
•	
•	
•	
•	
•	
•	
•	

SYMPOSIUM: Future Events That Will Require Courage

What must I do to maintain courage?:

Sunday - *"Be courageous and strong heart. Yes, hope in Jehovah"* - Psalm 27:14

9:40 The Destruction of Babylon the Great

Speaker:

Favorite Point:

Theme Scripture(s):

WHO IS BABYLON THE GREAT? WHAT SIGNS CAN I WATCH FOR?

Main Points / Scriptures	NOTES

Why is this such an important event?

SYMPOSIUM: Future Events That Will Require Courage

JWWorksheets.com
IG:@JWDownloads
JW-Downloads.com

55

9:40 The Proclamation of the Hailstone Message

Speaker:

Favorite Point:

Theme Scripture(s):

WHAT IS THE "HAILSTONE MESSAGE"?

Main Points

-
-
-

Scriptures

NOTES

Why is the term "hailstone" used:_____

SYMPOSIUM: Future Events That Will Require Courage

9:40 The Attack by Gog of Magog

Speaker:

Favorite Point:

Theme Scripture(s):

WHO IS GOG OF MAGOG?

WHAT IS THIS "ATTACK"?

Scriptures

Main Points

NOTES

(side) JWWorksheets.com — IG:@JWDownloads — JW-Downloads.com — Symposium: Future Events That Will Require Courage

9:40 Armageddon

Speaker:

Favorite Point:

Theme Scripture(s):

WHAT IS ARMAGEDDON?

Main Points / Scriptures	NOTES

A single point I want to remember:

How important is being courageous now?_____

(left margin) SYMPOSIUM: Future Events That Will Require Courage

9:40 The Great Reconstruction

Speaker:

Favorite Point:

Theme Scripture(s):

WHAT IS "THE GREAT RECONSTRUCTION"?

Main Points / Scriptures	NOTES

A single point I want to remember:

SYMPOSIUM: Future Events That Will Require Courage

Why is courage required for this event? :_____

9:40 SYMPOSIUM: Future Events That Will Require Courage
The Final Test

Speaker:

Favorite Point:

Theme Scripture(s):

WHAT IS "THE FINAL TEST"?

Main Points - Talk Summary

NOTES

SCRIPTURES

Something New I Learned:

11:20 PUBLIC DISCOURSE: The Resurrection Hope Imparts Courage - HOW?

Speaker:

Favorite Point:

Theme Scripture(s):

How does the Resurrection hope help you?

How can you use this in the ministry?

Scriptures

Main Points

NOTES

JWWorksheets.com

IG:@JWDownloads

JW-Downloads.com

Who are you looking forward to meeting in the new world?_____

1:50 FEATURE FILM: THE STORY OF JONAH - A Lesson in Courage and Mercy

Speaker:

Favorite Point:

Theme Scripture(s):

WHO WAS JONAH?

Scriptures referencing Jonah:

- _____
- _____
- _____
- _____
- _____
- _____
- _____

Most moving part:

NOTES

_____
_____
_____
_____
_____
_____
_____
_____
_____
_____

62 My "review" of the film: _____

2:50 There Are More With Us Than Against Us!

Speaker:

Favorite Point:

Theme Scripture(s):

WHO IS WITH US?

Main Points - Talk Summary

NOTES

SCRIPTURES

I am excited for the future because:_____

Armageddon	Future	Peace
Babylon	Gog	Proclamation
Bible	Hailstone	Public
Courage	Heart	Reconstruction
Courage	Hope	Resurrection
Courageous	Hope	Security
Destruction	Imparts	Strong
Discourse	Jehovah	Summary
Events	Jonah	Sunday
Feature	Magog	Symposium
Film	Mercy	Test
Final	Message	Watchtower

S M E W G Z G K S C K H I Q E R U T U F V A P
S M G Z T R X H I H H A A L H E A R T I W X Y
H A A I S Y F N A G N O R T S H V W A R I B Z
J N S J E N P O D V G Q Q E N O T S L I A H T
G C S O T Q L I X F O E K D O Y G W V S Y D L
O S E X G M W T E N J H L M V V U W E W E E Y
G L M M M Q N A X O N E E B X T E U G O S S Y
M S R B V R T M M I O N J J I J C U A C R T U
T H O B A U P A Y T D Q P E R B A U R E U R V
R F O G R S U L Q C D W K M E K E Z U N O U U
E I Y E H F B C H U E W G M S Y P D O C C E
W F X O M N L O U R G L N W U A Z Y C O S T T
O V I V R J I R K T A I U S R D W C I U I I I
T Z A N O H C P J S M F P U R N G R A R D O M
H T B N A Z Z N X N R M V M E U C E E A Q N P
C V A N V L E I S O A U M M C S I M D G S L A
T H B U M T G Z J C W I A A T D M U I E E V R
A L Y G O U A M S E G S G R I M O W C O V I T
W L L L Y U R A T R I O O Y O R L U Y U W S S
W N O H H U U X N W Y P G Q N Z R I E S N C N
X U N T O C O C E Y Z M G Z Y I X X F Z Y Q I
P E P O H P C Q V U V Y L M T A I D H C T J R
N T T Z M C E L E Y S S C Y D H G H E H W W J

SUNDAY REVIEW

What was the theme scripture for Friday and Saturday?

What is the "Hailstone Message"?

How does the Resurrection hope give courage?

What was your favorite part of the Feature Film?

Reflections on the Convention:

Friends I saw that I haven't seen in a while:

Friends I want to get together/catch up with:

Friends that need encouragement/help:

A friend I want to share my favorite points with:

JWWorksheets.com

IG:@JWDownloads

JW-Downloads.com

B
E

C
O
U
R
A
G
E
O
U
S